Chapter 1
Severe Weather

 **Think!**

 Read the key points. When you finish, check t.

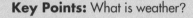

Key Points: What is weather?

When you wake up in the morning, before you start to get ready for the day, you probably look outside to check the weather. You need to know if it is raining or sunny and if it will be hot or cold. Knowing the weather will help you prepare for the day.

But what exactly is weather? **Weather** is a combination of short-term events that happen each day in the layer of gas surrounding the Earth, called the **atmosphere**. Weather is different in different parts of the world and it changes over minutes, hours, days, or weeks. These changes are caused by factors such as temperature and winds.

You may already know that weather can refer to the temperature outside, the amount of sunlight, and the amount of precipitation such as rain or snow in an area. But, weather can also include factors such as wind speed; how much moisture is in the air, or its humidity; and atmospheric pressure, or the force produced by the gases surrounding the Earth.

 Complete the exercise.

Test your knowledge

(1) Which best describes weather?

A. We can only learn the weather by watching TV.

B. Weather is a combination of short-term events that happen each day in our atmosphere.

C. Weather is the same every day, and is not affected by temperature and wind.

Ans. ☐

(2) Which is not a factor of weather?

A. amount of sunlight	B. precipitation	C. weight	D. wind speed	E. temperature

Ans. ☐

J
500
Kumon
STEM Missions: Earth Science

9/30/2020
ING/IP
$8.95

Chapter 1
Severe Weather

What types of weather do you experience most days? Have you ever experienced severe weather?

 Read the key points below. When you finish, check the box.

Key Points: Types of Severe Weather

In some cases, severe weather conditions can develop. **Severe weather** is any weather event that can threaten a community's safety or cause damage to people and property. Some examples of severe weather events can include heat waves, droughts, blizzards, and powerful hurricanes or cyclones.

One of the most common types of severe weather is a thunderstorm. Thunderstorms can cause weather events such as lightning, hail, strong winds, flooding and even tornadoes. If you live in an area where thunderstorms are common, you may have experienced some of these events.

Lightning: Lightning is the release of electricity that happens high in the atmosphere, or in-between the atmosphere and the ground. Lightning forms during severe thunderstorms from charged particles in the air. If lightning strikes the ground it can start fires and damage buildings.

Tornadoes: A tornado is a dangerous rotating column of air created by the strong winds of a thunderstorm. If a tornado gets large enough to reach the ground it can cause terrible damage to buildings, vehicles, trees, and anything else in its path.

Hail: Pieces of ice that fall from clouds during a severe thunderstorm are called hail. Hail can be different sizes, from a pebble to a golf ball or even the size of a softball! Large pieces of hail can be dangerous and cause damage to cars, buildings, and trees.

Strong winds: Thunderstorms can create winds up to 100 miles per hour! These winds can knock over trees and break windows.

Flash flooding: Flash flooding is also a concern during a severe thunderstorm. If a lot of rain falls quickly and the ground cannot absorb it, an area can flood quickly. Heavy rain is a common cause of flooding during a thunderstorm.

 Complete the exercise.

Test your knowledge

Match the type of severe weather to the description. Choose the correct answer from the box below.

A: lightning   B: hail   C: tornado   D. flash flooding

(1) A dangerous, rotating column of strong wind.

Ans.

(2) Pieces of ice that fall from a thunderstorm.

Ans.

(3) Electricity released from a thunderstorm created by charged particles in the air.

Ans.

(4) When heavy rain causes water to build up instead of being absorbed by the ground.

Ans.

Chapter 1
Severe Weather

Think!

Which type of warning system would be the best for alerting people to an incoming tornado?

Check!

📖 Read the key points below. When you finish, check the box.

Key Points: Severe Weather Safety

When it comes to staying safe during severe weather events, like a thunderstorm, there are some solutions and safety measures available. For example, storm proof windows made with reinforced glass were created to help limit the damage caused by strong winds. In areas where hurricanes are more likely to happen, people sometimes put hurricane shutters on their houses to help decrease window damage. These inventions have proven to be effective for preventing damage to buildings.

While limiting the damage to buildings is important, scientists and engineers also focus on developing ways to keep people safe. This led to the development of warning systems that alert people to incoming dangerous storms so they can prepare or move somewhere safe. One example of this type of precaution is a siren warning system.

Siren warning systems can quickly send a message across a town or city to warn of possible danger. These systems produce a loud sound that informs people of a severe weather event. These systems were used as the primary alert method before TVs and phones were common. Sirens typically have a separate power source in case a storm causes the power to go out. This allows them to alert communities when phones and TVs don't work.

More recently, scientists and engineers have developed alert system that can be sent to cell phones to alert people of severe weather events. These alert messages are the quickest and most reliable way to inform people of possible severe weather events. Knowing about dangerous weather early on gives people and communities time to prepare and get to safety.

✏️ Complete the exercise.

Test your knowledge

Answer T for true or F for false.

(1) Hurricane shutters can reduce damage to windows.

Ans. ☐

(2) The siren warning system does not work if power is lost due to severe weather.

Ans. ☐

(3) Engineers are constantly working on solutions to protect us to people from severe weather.

Ans. ☐

Severe Weather

 Use the word box below to fill in the blanks and review key vocabulary.

Review the Key Points

Weather is a combination of short-term events that happen each day in the layer of gas surrounding the Earth, called the [_____]. Weather is different in different parts of the world and it changes over minutes, hours, days, or weeks. These changes are caused by factors such as temperature and winds.

You may already know that weather can refer to the temperature outside, the amount of sunlight, and the amount of precipitation such as rain or snow in an area. But, weather can also include factors such as wind speed; how much moisture is in the air, or its humidity; and atmospheric pressure, or the force produced by the gases surrounding the Earth. [_____] is any weather event that can threaten a community's safety or cause damage to people and property.

When it comes to staying safe during severe weather events, like a thunderstorm, there are some solutions and safety measures available. For example, storm proof windows made with reinforced glass were created to help limit the damage caused by strong winds. In areas where hurricanes are more likely to happen, people sometimes put hurricane [_____] on their houses to help decrease window damage.

While limiting the damage to buildings is important, scientists and engineers also focus on developing ways to keep people safe. This led to the development of warning systems that [_____] people to incoming dangerous storms so they can prepare or move somewhere safe. One example of this type of precaution is a siren warning system.

severe weather / atmosphere / alert / shutters

Complete the exercise.

Math Mission

Temperature can sometimes be an indicator that severe weather is likely to occur. Answer the following questions about the three thermometers on the right.

(1) What is the temperature indicated by thermometer A?

Ans. [_____] °F

(2) Find the difference between the temperatures indicated by thermometers B and C.

Ans. [_____] °F

(3) Find the difference between the highest and lowest temperatures.

Ans. [_____] °F

Severe Weather

 Read the mission. Then, answer the following questions to help you with your solution.

The Mission

Severe weather like thunderstorms, tornadoes, and hurricanes can cause terrible damage to buildings, homes, and communities. They can leave people without power, fresh water, food, or shelter. Design a system or a device that can protect a house from the dangerous effects of a thunderstorm.

Before you design...THINK!

1. Describe the mission in your own words.

2. Brainstorm about a solution. Write your notes in the space below. Use the following questions to guide your thinking:

   (1) What type of prevention technology would you use?
   (2) Can you improve on current devices? Or create a new solution?
   (3) Can you create your own design to stop hail or tornado damage?

Severe Weather

Read the mission. Then, draw and evaluate your solution.

The Mission

Design a system or a device that can protect a house from the dangerous effects of a thunderstorm.

Design

Draw or write about your solution below.

Evaluate

Evaluate your severe weather protection system. Do you think it would work? Did you choose to create a new device or improve an existing one?

Beach Erosion

Think!

What is erosion?

Check

 Read the key points. When you finish, check the box.

Key Points: Erosion and Weathering

Have you ever looked at the landscape around you and wondered if it looks the same as it did 1,000 years ago? The answer is no! The Earth's features were shaped over many years by natural processes called weathering and erosion.

Weathering is the breaking down of rock and solid landforms into smaller pieces. **Erosion** is the process that transports the smaller pieces of rock, soil, and sand from one location to another. One of the main forces on Earth that causes erosion is water. Some other sources of erosion are wind, glacial, chemical, temperature, and human activities.

Water erosion is when pieces of rock, sand, or loose soil are carried or worn away by water.

Wind erosion is when wind moves loose rock, soil, and sand from one place to another.

Glacial erosion is when a slow moving mass of ice called a glacier moves across the land carrying away rock and soil.

Chemical erosion is when chemical substances such as acid rain erode the Earth's

features into smaller landforms.

Temperature erosion is when the temperature in an area is so extreme that it causes the Earth to expand and crack into pieces, which can get carried away.

Erosion by people is when human actions such as land development and foot traffic can cause erosion.

Erosion shapes the landscape around us. A great example of erosion is the Grand Canyon. It was formed as the water of the Colorado River and wind carved away at the canyon walls over a period of 5 to 6 million years!

The Grand Canyon in the US was created by erosion.

 Complete the exercise.

Test your knowledge

Choose the best word to complete each sentence.

(1) The breaking up of earth and rocks into small pieces is called (weathering / erosion).

Ans.

(2) The carrying away of small pieces of rock, soil, and sand from one place to another is called (weathering / erosion).

Ans.

(3) Erosion caused by activities such as land development and foot traffic is erosion by (people / water).

Ans.

Chapter 2
Beach Erosion

Think!

What happens when erosion is sped up in a certain place, like a beach or coastline?

 Read the key points below. When you finish, check the box.

Check

Key Points: Beach Erosion

Beach erosion is the loss of beach sand typically caused by water and wind movement. Sand is washed away from the beach, and moved farther out to sea or to another beach or coastline. This process can greatly reduce the size of a beach. Strong winds can also cause a beach to erode by blowing grains of sand away.

These factors are why hurricanes can be very bad for beaches. Hurricanes can produce strong winds and create big waves that wash away more sand from the beach than normal weathering does. It is very common to see severe erosion to beaches and coastlines after a hurricane or a strong thunderstorm.

Although beach erosion is mainly caused by natural weathering, there are times when human activities can lead to increased beach erosion. When people walk through the delicate grass or dune areas that often surround beaches, they can accidentally harm the native plants that grow there. As these native plants are damaged or removed, erosion can increase because the plant's roots help hold the beach sand in place. Without them, sand can be more easily carried away by wind or water.

 Complete the exercise.

Test your knowledge

Answer T for true or F for false.

(1) Beach erosion is the increase of the size of a beach due to sand movement by wind and water.

Ans. ☐

(2) Strong winds may speed up erosion.

Ans. ☐

(3) Erosion can be stopped by removing plants native to a beach.

Ans. ☐

Chapter 2
Beach Erosion

Think!

Why do engineers study the effects of erosion?

📖 Read the key points below. When you finish, check the box.

Key Points: Erosion Prevention

Erosion has been shaping coastlines for millions of years. The real problems come after a severe storm hits, when human activity speeds up erosion, or when buildings and roads are close enough to the ocean to be damaged by the effects of erosion. In some cases, beach erosion can cause flooding, and can even make a whole building collapse as the land it stands on is washed away.

Fortunately, scientists and engineers have studied erosion in order to create ways to help protect the environment, structures, and people from the damage it can cause. Here are some of the devices and methods that were developed to help communities that are facing problems due to erosion.

A house in danger of falling into the ocean because of beach erosion.

Redistributing Sand:
This method uses large trucks to bring in extra sand and dump it in the areas that are more prone to having sand washed away. This method is often used after hurricanes to help rebuild beaches.

Building windbreaks:
Windbreaks are fences that keep sand from blowing away in the wind. These fences can help keep a natural level of sand on the beach.

Using erosion control mats:
These mats stabilize the sand in an area long enough for plants to grow roots. The plant's roots help hold the sand and soil in place making it harder to erode away.

✏️ Complete the exercise.

Test your knowledge

Match the beach erosion prevention action with its definition.

> **A. Redistributing sand**   **B. Building windbreaks**   **C. Using erosion control mats**

(1) They are designed to help grow native plants that hold beach sand in place.

Ans. ____

(2) They prevent sand from being blown away by the wind.

Ans. ____

(3) This method carries the sand by truck to a place where beach sand is likely to be washed away.

Ans. ____

Beach Erosion

✏️ Use the word box below to fill in the blanks and review key vocabulary.

Review the Key Points

The Earth's features were shaped over many years by natural processes called weathering and erosion.

[_____] is the breaking down of rock and solid landforms into smaller pieces.

[_____] is the process that transports the smaller pieces of rock, soil, and sand from one location to another. One of the main forces on Earth that causes erosion is water. Some other sources of erosion are wind, glacial, chemical, temperature, and human activities.

Beach erosion is the loss of [_____] typically caused by water and wind movement. Sand is washed away from the beach, and moved further out to sea or to another beach or coastline. This process can greatly reduce the size of a beach. [_____] can also cause a beach to erode by blowing grains of sand away.

Fortunately, scientists and engineers have studied erosion in order to create ways to help protect the environment, structures, and people from the damage it can cause.

> beach sand / erosion / weathering / strong winds

🖩 Complete the exercise.

Math Mission

Answer the questions about erosion conditions to see how quickly erosion can change the landscape.

(1) Beaches on the south shore of New York's Long Island are eroding. About 2 feet of beach disappears each year. How many feet will erode in the next ten years?

Ans. [_____] feet

(2) If 6 inches of soil erode each year, how many years would it take for 36 inches of soil to erode from a hillside?

Ans. [_____] years

(3) Engineers are trying to rebuild a beach in North Carolina. If a dump truck can carry 4 tons of sand to add to the beach, how many truck loads would it take to bring 24 tons of sand to the beach?

Ans. [_____] trucks

Beach Erosion

 Read the mission. Then, answer the following questions to help you with your solution.

The Mission

You show up one summer to your favorite beach and find that a hurricane hit the beach during the year and eroded much of the beach away. Develop a plan to prevent the beach from eroding further and to help restore it to the way it was before.

Before you design...THINK!

1. Describe the mission in your own words.

2. Brainstorm a solution. Write your notes in the space below.

   Use the following questions to guide your thinking:

   (1) What are some methods for preventing beach erosion that you read about in this chapter?

   (2) What factors should you consider? Do you need to stop wind or water weathering? Or can you design something to prevent the erosion in the first place?

Beach Erosion

💡 Read the mission. Then, draw and evaluate your solution.

The Mission

Develop a plan to prevent the beach from eroding further and to help restore it to the way it was before.

Design   Draw or write about your solution below.

Evaluate

Evaluate your design. What is one thing about your design that could be improved? Did you consider educating the community about how some erosion is caused by people as part of your plan?

Chapter 3
Tectonic Plates

Think!

Do you know why mountains rise so high above the Earth's surface?

Check

📖 Read the key points. When you finish, check the box.

Key Points: What are Tectonic Plates?

Did you know the Earth's outer layer, or crust, is not solid like an egg shell? Scientists have learned that the Earth's crust is broken up into pieces called **tectonic plate**s that float on top of the **magma**, or hot melted rock, which makes up an inner layer of the Earth called the **mantle**.

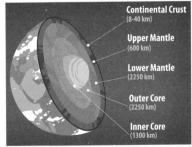

Continental Crust (8-40 km)
Upper Mantle (600 km)
Lower Mantle (2250 km)
Outer Core (2250 km)
Inner Core (1300 km)

Section of the Earth's Crust

Tectonic Plates

When the Earth's tectonic plates move, they create different features on the Earth's surface. Their movement is responsible for most of the Earth's features such as mountains and ocean trenches.

Tectonic plates can move against each other in different ways: they can slide past each other, slide over the top of each other, slide under each other, and move away from each other.

Plate Movement

For example, two plates pushing up against each other has led to the creation of mountain ranges around the world, from the Rocky Mountains in North America to the Himalayan Mountains in Asia. When two plates move away from each other they can create trenches, like the deep Mariana Trench in the Pacific Ocean.

Rocky Mountains in Colorado, USA

✏️ Complete the exercise.

Test your knowledge

Answer the questions using the passage for help.

(1) What are tectonic plates?
A. pieces of the Earth's crust that fit together like a puzzle
B. the inner most layer of the Earth
C. what mountains are made of
D. the layer of earth on the ocean floor

Ans. ▢

(2) Which is not a layer of the Earth?
A. crust   B. mantle   C. sky   D. core

Ans. ▢

Tectonic Plates

Think!

What causes an earthquake?

Check

📖 Read the key points below. When you finish, check the box.

Key Points: What is an earthquake?

Since the plates are floating on top of the moving magma that makes up the mantle, they are constantly moving and changing the Earth's landscape and the ocean floors. This constant movement is what can lead to destructive events, like earthquakes.

An **earthquake** is an event caused when two plates slip past or rub against each other, under the Earth's surface and create pressure. The point where they slip is called a **fault** or a **fault plane**. When enough pressure builds up along a fault plane an earthquake can occur. This causes the land around it to shake suddenly and violently which can cause major damage to everything surrounding it.

Cracked road after an earthquake

Earthquakes can destroy buildings, cause injuries, and cause changes to the land surrounding the fault zone.

There are some areas in the world that are more likely to experience earthquakes because these areas are along or near fault lines in the Earth's crust. Some examples are the west coast of the United States, countries in the Pacific Ocean like Japan and Indonesia, and middle east countries like Turkey and Iran.

Buildings destroyed by an earthquake

✏️ Complete the exercise.

Test your knowledge

Answer the questions below based on the reading.

(1) What causes an earthquake?
A. the Earth's rotation around the sun
B. the rise and fall of ocean tides
C. the pieces of the Earth's crust moving against each other
D. the Earth's gravity

Ans. ☐

(2) What is a fault or fault plane?
A. a place where a mountain begins   B. a place where two plates move against each other
C. a place where the Earth's crust separates   D. a place where there is no solid land

Ans. ☐

(3) Why are some areas more likely to have an earthquake than others?
A. they have more solid land   B. they are along the ocean
C. they have more mountains   D. they are along fault lines in the Earth's crust

Ans. ☐

Chapter 3
Tectonic Plates

Think!

How can we help lessen earthquake damage?

Check

📖 **Read the key points below. When you finish, check the box.**

Key Points: Earthquake Safety

The most damage occurs at the center of the earthquake, or the **epicenter**. This is where an earthquake is the strongest. Since earthquakes cannot be predicted, scientists have developed tools to help measure their magnitude. Scientists use a device called a **seismograph** to measure the movement and vibrations, or seismic waves of earthquakes. The length of the lines recorded shows the size of the seismic waves and the strength of the earthquake that caused them. It is important to study the strength and vibrations of an earthquake, so we can determine how to help keep communities safe when they occur.

In communities where earthquakes are more likely to happen, like southern California, scientists and engineers work together to make buildings stronger and help lessen the damage caused by an earthquake. Here are a few examples:

One traditional way to help prevent earthquake damage to a building is by reinforcing the structure. This is typically done with shear walls, cross-beams, and horizontal frames that help keep the building stable during seismic waves.

Another option is to build a flexible foundation using rubber, lead, and steel underneath a building that will absorb the seismic waves and help the building stay stable.

Seismic rings are a newer option for earthquake protection. They are made of plastic or concrete and are placed underground around a building. They are designed to help channel the shock waves from an earthquake and move them around the building instead of through it.

Reinforced Building with Steel Braces

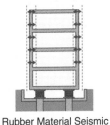
Rubber Material Seismic Isolation Device Under a Building

✏️ **Complete the exercise.**

Test your knowledge

Answer the questions below about the reading.

(1) Where does most earthquake damage occur?

A. the fault plane   B. the epicenter   C. the furthest from the epicenter

Ans. ☐

(2) What is a seismograph?

A. a device used to measure seismic waves
B. a device used to measure earthquake damage
C. a device used to predict earthquakes
D. a device used to measure the distance an earthquake travels

Ans. ☐

Chapter 3
Tectonic Plates

 Use the word box below to fill in the blanks and review key vocabulary.

Review the Key Points

Scientists have learned that the Earth's crust is broken up into pieces called tectonic plates that float on top of the magma, or hot melted rock, which makes up an inner layer of the Earth called the [   ].

When the Earth's tectonic plates move, they create different features on the Earth's surface. Their movement is responsible for most of the Earth's features such as mountains and ocean trenches. [   ] can move against each other in different ways: they can slide past each other, slide over the top of each other, slide under each other, and move away from each other.

An [   ] is an event caused when two plates slip past or rub against each other, under the Earth's surface and create pressure. The point where they slip is called a fault or a fault plane.

When enough pressure builds up along a fault plane an earthquake can occur. This causes the land around it to shake suddenly and violently which can cause major damage to everything surrounding it.

The most damage occurs at the center of the earthquake, or the [   ]. This is where an earthquake is the strongest. Since earthquakes cannot be predicted, scientists have developed tools to help measure their magnitude. Scientists use a device called a [   ] to measure the movement and vibrations, or seismic waves of earthquakes. The length of the lines recorded shows the size of the seismic waves and the strength of the earthquake that caused them. It is important to study the strength and vibrations of an earthquake, so we can determine how to help keep communities safe when they occur.

> epicenter / earthquake / mantle / tectonic plates / seismograph

Complete the exercise.

Math Mission

Scientists are constantly reviewing graphs and charts of old earthquake activity to help them better understand earthquakes and how to keep people safe. Use the chart to answer the questions below.

(1) How many magnitude 5 earthquakes happen each year?

Ans. [   ]

(2) What magnitude earthquakes happen the most often?
   A. magnitude 4   B. magnitude 6   C. magnitude 8

Ans. [   ]

(3) What magnitude earthquakes happen the least often?
   A. magnitude 4   B. magnitude 6   C. magnitude 8

Ans. [   ]

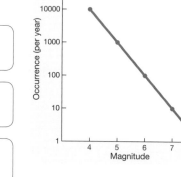

World wide earthquakes

Tectonic Plates

 Read the mission. Then, answer the following questions to help you with your solution.

The Mission

Imagine you live in a community that is at high risk for earthquake activity. Design a way to prevent damage to your home from an earthquake.

You can make changes to your home, the land around it, or the tools you will use.

Before you design...THINK!

1. Describe the mission in your own words.

2. Brainstorm about a solution. Write your notes in the space below.

    Use the following questions to guide your thinking:

    (1) What type of prevention technology would you use?
    (2) Can you improve on current devices? Or create a new solution?

Chapter 3
Tectonic Plates

💡 Read the mission. Then, draw and evaluate your solution.

The Mission

Design a way to prevent damage to your home from an earthquake.
You can make changes to your home, the land around it, or the tools you
will use.

Design

Draw or write your solution below.

Evaluate

Consider your solution: What technology did you use to help reinforce your dwelling? Did you
improve on something that already exists? Or did you invent your own solution?

Chapter 4
Flooding

Think!

What is a flood? And what causes a flood?

Check!

 Read the key points. When you finish, check the box.

Key Points: What causes flooding?

Do you remember playing in puddles after a rainstorm when you were younger? Puddles often form when there is too much rain for the ground to absorb or there is nowhere for the water to drain. While small puddles are fun to play in, too much rain can be dangerous. When rain falls and it isn't absorbed by the ground or has no place to drain, it can cause a **flood**. A flood is a type of natural disaster that happens when water quickly covers land that is usually dry.

Flooding is caused by heavy rain from severe storms as you learned in Chapter 1. But, it can also be caused by a large amount of snow melting quickly, overflowing rivers, and other severe weather events such as hurricanes.

There are different types of floods. Some can be good for an area while others can be devastating.

A river flood happens when the banks or sides of a river overflow. This can damage nearby streets, cars, and buildings. However, rivers in some areas do flood each year and help create land that is good for farming. Flood waters can carry nutrients that enrich the soil.

A flash flood happens when heavy rainfall causes a lot of water to flow through a river or stream very fast. Flash floods can also happen in city streets, if rain falls too fast for drainage systems to keep up. This type of flood is very dangerous because it can happen so quickly that people do not have time to get to safety and can get swept away and injured by the fast moving water.

A coastal flood happens when storms cause the water along a coastline to rise above the beach level. This can cause damage to beaches and manmade structures.

 Complete the exercise.

Test your knowledge

Choose one of the following sentences that contains errors.

A. Floods can occur when a lot of rain falls and the rain is not absorbed by the ground.

B. Floods are not caused by severe weather events like hurricanes.

C. There are various types of floods, such as river floods, flash floods, and coastal floods.

Ans.

Flooding

Think!

What are some problems flooding can cause?

Check

 Read the key points below. When you finish, check the box.

Key Points: Effects of Floods

Flooding can be disastrous for communities. Below are some examples of the problems flooding can cause.

Effects of Floods on Structures:
Flood waters can cause mold to grow in houses and buildings. This can cause houses to rot, which can make structures unsafe for people to live in or work in.

Effects of Floods on Water Supplies:
Flooding can also damage sewer systems and cause waste to get into a community's drinking water supplies. This can make people sick if they drink contaminated water.

Effects of Floods on Human Health:
Floods can bring pests, like mosquitoes who like to lay their eggs in still water. These pests can multiply quickly and carry diseases like the Zika virus or malaria which can make people very sick.

Mosquitoes can carry diseases

Effects of Floods on the Environment:
Flood waters can sometimes be helpful to the areas around them. When a river floods, it leaves behind nutrients that soak into the soil and create good farmland. A floodplain is an area surrounding a river that naturally absorbs flood waters.

Mississippi River floodplain

 Complete the exercise.

Test your knowledge

Match each problem caused by flooding to the dangerous effects it can have on people.

(1) mosquitoes ●

● contaminated drinking water

(2) mold and rot  ●

● diseases like the Zika virus or malaria

(3) damaged sewer systems  ●

● structures that are unsafe to live in

Chapter 4
Flooding

Think!

What are some ways we can protect ourselves from flooding?

Check

 Read the key points below. When you finish, check the box.

Key Points: Ways to Prevent Flood Damage

Engineers have designed systems to control flooding such as dams, levees, and dikes that help keep fast-moving and dangerous flood waters away from buildings and structures. By stopping flood waters or controlling their movement, we can keep our communities safe.

Dams:
A dam is a wall or structure designed to hold back water or prevent it from flowing. One side of a dam often forms a reservoir, a type of lake that stores water for people to use. Reservoirs supply communities with water and power.

Levees:
A levee is an embankment or ridge built to stop a river from overflowing its banks onto dry land. Some levees are created naturally by soil and rocks that are deposited on a river's banks as it flows. A levee can also be manmade, by building up the sides of a river with dirt, sand, or cement.

Dikes:
A dike is a long wall or ditch built to prevent flood waters from damaging surrounding communities. Dikes are built to protect communities where flood water might naturally accumulate or drain into land now inhabited by people.

 Complete the exercise.

Test your knowledge

Match the type of flood barrier to its definition.

(1) A wall or structure built across a body of water to hold water back.

(2) A long wall or ditch built to prevent flood water from flooding an area.

(3) An embankment, natural or manmade, built to stop a river from overflowing its banks.

dam

levee

dike

Chapter 4
Flooding

✏️ Use the word box below to fill in the blanks and review key vocabulary.

Review the Key Points

When rain falls and it isn't absorbed by the ground or has no place to drain, it can cause a [   ]. A flood is a type of natural disaster that happens when water quickly covers land that is usually dry.

Flooding is caused by [   ] from severe storms as you learned in Chapter 1. But, it can also be caused by a large amount of snow melting quickly, overflowing rivers, and other severe weather events such as hurricanes.

Flooding can be disastrous for communities and cause harm to structures, water supplies, and people's health.

Flood waters can sometimes be helpful to the areas around them. When a river floods, it leaves behind nutrients that soak into the soil and create good farmland. A [   ] is an area surrounding a river that naturally absorbs flood waters.

Engineers have designed systems to control flooding such as dams (a wall or structure designed to hold water or prevent it from flowing), levees (an embankment or ridge built to stop a river from overflowing), and [   ] (a long wall or ditch built to stop flood waters) that help keep fast moving and dangerous flood waters away from buildings and structures. By stopping flood waters or controlling their movement we can keep our communities safe.

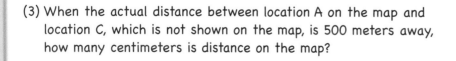

heavy rain / floodplain / dikes / flood

🧮 Complete the exercise.

Math Mission

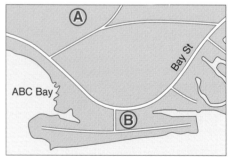

The map to the right shows which areas have a higher risk of flooding due to how close they are to shore. Answer the question below using the map. Remember on a map distance is always to scale: 1 cm = 100 m.

(1) Which of the locations, A and B, on the map is less likely to be at risk of flooding?

Ans.  location ____

(2) If the distance between locations A and B is 3 centimeters (cm) on the map, how many meters (m) is the actual distance?

Ans. [   ] m

(3) When the actual distance between location A on the map and location C, which is not shown on the map, is 500 meters away, how many centimeters is distance on the map?

Ans. [   ] cm

Chapter 4
Flooding

 Read the mission. Then, answer the following questions to help you with your solution.

The Mission

Imagine you live near a large river that commonly floods. Design a new piece of technology or develop a plan to prevent some of the possible problems caused by flooding that you learned about it this chapter.

Before you design...THINK!

1. Describe the mission in your own words.

2. Brainstorm about a solution. Write your notes in the space below.

   Use the following questions to guide your thinking:

   (1) Can you use existing flood prevention tools in your plan? Or will you need to develop a new tool?

   (2) What type of flooding problem do you want to focus on?

Flooding

💡 Read the mission. Then, draw and evaluate your solution.

The Mission

Imagine you live near a large river that commonly floods. Design a new piece of technology or develop a plan to prevent some of the possible problems caused by flooding that you learned about it this chapter.

Design

Draw or about write your solution below.

Evaluate

Evaluate your flood prevention or protection system. Do you think it would work? Why or why not? Can you think of anything else you could add to make your plan more successful?

Chapter 5
Changing Climates

 Think!

What is climate? What causes different areas to have different climates?

 Check

 Read the key points. When you finish, check the box.

Key Points: What is climate?

Climate is the pattern of weather over a period of time in a certain area. For example, the climate near the equator is warm and wet for most of the year. Climate does not change from day to day like weather, as you learned in Chapter 1. An area's climate is specific to its location and the people, animals, and plants that live there are adapted to their climates.

There are several things that affect the climate of an area. These factors are the landscape of an area, how close or far from bodies of water like lakes or oceans an area is, an area's latitude, or location on the Earth's surface, and an area's height above sea level. These factors cause changes to the temperature, humidity, wind speed, or the type and amount of precipitation, such as rain or snow, that an area gets.

The distance above sea level is an important factor in determining an area's climate. The higher the area is above sea level, the colder and drier it often is, like Denver, CO in the U.S. Places that are closer to sea level typically have more warm and wet weather like the Hawaiian Islands in the U.S.

Denver, CO USA

Hawaiian Islands, USA

 Complete the exercise.

Test your knowledge

Answer T for true or F for false.

(1) The climate is the weather pattern in a specific area, and it changes daily like the weather.

Ans. ☐

(2) The latitude of an area on the Earth is one of the factors that affects the local climate.

Ans. ☐

(3) The higher the area is above sea level, the more warm and dry it tends to be.

Ans. ☐

Chapter 5
Changing Climates

Think! What type of climate do you live in? Do you have hot summers or freezing winters? A lot rain or very little rain?

 Read the key points below. When you finish, check the box.

Key Points: Climates around the World

There are different types of climates around the world such as Polar, Temperate, Tropical, Continental, Dry, and others.

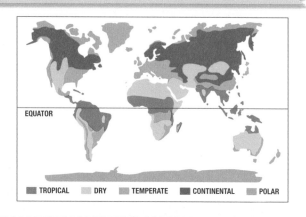

EQUATOR

■ TROPICAL ■ DRY ■ TEMPERATE ■ CONTINENTAL ■ POLAR

Polar Climate Zone
- cold temperatures all year
- short summers and long winters
- warm months are less than 50 °F degrees
- Examples: Northern coastal regions of North America, Greenland, and Antarctica

Temperate Climate Zone
- hot summers and cold winters
- four distinct seasons
- varying precipitation rain, snow, sleet...etc.
- Examples: New England in North America and Central Europe

Tropical Climate Zone
- large amounts of rainfall each year
- warm and wet for most of the year
- closest to the equator
- Average temp: greater than 64 °F year round
- Examples: South America, Hawaiian Island in NA, and parts of Africa

Dry Climate Zone
- dry and arid conditions
- less than 12 inches of rain per year
- Examples: Southern North America, Africa, and Australia

Continental Climate Zone
- Warm to cool summers and very cold winters
- Intense snowstorms, strong winds and temperatures below −22 °F
- Examples: the Polar Climate in places like Canada in the North America and Russia in Europe

Other Climate Zones – These main climate zones can be separated into smaller categories like:
- **Highland Zone** - where temperature and weather changes quickly as the distance above sea level rises
- **Subtropics Zone** - where the temperature is more mild than humid tropics, with less rainfall
- **Coastal Zone** - where there are cool winters and warm summers and the temperature does not get too hot or too cold

 Complete the exercise.

Test your knowledge

Match the climate zone to the example pictured below.

A. polar climate **B. temperate climate** **C. tropical climate** **D. dry climate**

(1)

Ans.

(2)

Ans.

(3)

Ans.

(4)

Ans.

Chapter 5
Changing Climates

Think!

Since climate is the weather of an area over time, can it change like the weather does?

Check!

 Read the key points below. When you finish, check the box.

Key Points: What causes climates to change?

According to the National Oceanic and Atmospheric Association, or NOAA, climates all over the world are changing. Polar climates that were once never warmer than 50 °F in the summer are now seeing summer temperatures of 65 °F and higher. This is due to a process called global warming.

Global warming is a process that causes the average temperature on Earth to increase or warm up because of extra gas trapped in the atmosphere. When too many of these gases like carbon dioxide, methane, ozone, nitrous oxide and others are in the atmosphere, they trap the sun's heat and the temperature of the Earth begins to rise. This is called the **greenhouse effect**. This change in our global climate has a negative effect on people, animals, and plants around world because we are all adapted to, or prepared for, the climates we live in. Scientists believe this process is also causing more severe weather events like thunderstorms, hurricanes, droughts, and forest fires. This can make our living conditions on Earth unstable.

While no one is 100% sure what is causing the Earth's atmosphere to warm up, most scientists believe it's because of the pollution created by people's actions.

When we burn fossil fuels like coal and oil to create energy, as you'll learn in Chapter 7, we are adding to the greenhouse gases. So when we use gas to drive a car or burn coal to cook dinner we are adding to the pollution that causes global warming.

Another factor that could be adding to the rising global temperatures is deforestation, or the clearing of trees and plants from large areas so people can build on it. Trees and plants are what turn the carbon dioxide we breathe out back into oxygen we can breathe in. With less trees and plants less carbon dioxide is changed and it instead adds to the air pollution that is warming the atmosphere.

 Complete the exercise.

Test your knowledge

Answer T for true or F for false.

(1) Global warming is a process that causes the average temperature on Earth to increase or warm up because of extra gas trapped in the atmosphere.

Ans. [ ]

(2) The various actions of people have no effect on global warming at all.

Ans. [ ]

(3) The extra gases in the atmosphere have a negative impact on the Earth by trapping the sun's heat and causing the Earth's temperature to start rising.

Ans. [ ]

Chapter 5
Changing Climates

✎ Use the word box below to fill in the blanks and review key vocabulary.

Review the Key Points

_____ is the pattern of weather over a period of time in a certain area. Climate does not change from day to day like weather, as you learned in Chapter 1. An area's climate is specific to its location and the people, animals, and plants that live there are adapted to their climates.

There are several things that affect the climate of an area. These factors are the landscape of an area, how close or far from bodies of water like lakes or oceans an area is, an area's latitude, or location on the Earth's surface, and an area's height above _____. These factors cause changes to the temperature, humidity, wind speed, or the type and amount of precipitation, such as rain or snow, that an area gets.

There are different types of climates around the world such as Polar, Temperate, Tropical, Continental, Dry, and others.

_____ is a process that causes the average temperature on Earth to increase or warm up because of extra gas trapped in the atmosphere. When too many of these gases like carbon dioxide, methane, ozone, nitrous oxide and others are in the atmosphere, they trap the sun's heat and the temperature of the Earth begins to rise. This is called the _____. This change in our global climate has a negative effect on people, animals, and plants around world because we are all adapted to, or prepared for, the climates we live in.

While no one is 100% sure what is causing the Earth's atmosphere to warm up, most scientists believe it's because of the pollution created by people's actions.

> greenhouse effect / sea level / global warming / climate

🖩 Complete the exercise.

Math Mission

A plan is being implemented to restore the forest by planting seedlings in areas where many trees are cut down each year. It takes three minutes for one adult to plant a single sapling. Answer the following questions.

(1) How long does it take an adult to plant five saplings?

Ans. _____ minutes

(2) How many saplings can an adult plant in 60 minutes?

Ans. _____ saplings

(3) How many saplings can three adults plant in 30 minutes?

Ans. _____ saplings

Changing Climates

 Read the mission. Then, answer the following questions to help you with your solution.

The Mission

Climate change has a negative effect on our environment. Rising temperatures can hurt us, the Earth, and plants and animals around us. Create a plan to help inform the people in your community about climate zones and climate change.

Before you design...THINK!

1. Describe the mission in your own words.

2. Brainstorm about a solution. Write your notes in the space below. Use the following questions to guide your thinking:

   (1) How can you inform your town about the dangers of global warming?
   (2) How would you get everyone to follow your plan?

Changing Climates

💡 Read the mission. Then, draw and evaluate your solution.

The Mission

Climate change has a negative effect on our environment. Rising temperatures can hurt us, the Earth, and plants and animals around us. Create a plan to help inform the people in your community about climate zones and climate change.

Design

Draw or write your solution below.

Evaluate

How would your plan work? Do you think you would be successful? What is something you can change about your plan?

Landslides

Think!

Do you know what a landslide is?

Check

 Read the key points. When you finish, check the box.

Key Points: What is a landslide?

Have you ever built a tower out of blocks, and as you went to stack the last block on top, you bumped the tower, causing all the blocks to come crashing down? This experience is similar to what happens when a landslide occurs.

A **landslide** is a large movement of material, such as rock, soil, or mud, down the slope of a hill, a cliff, or a mountainside. And, just like your falling block tower, landslides can happen suddenly, due to changes in the stability or strength of their slopes. Although, sometimes land moves slowly down a mountainside over a longer period of time.

When a landslide happens it can cause serious damage to the surrounding land and communities, by blocking roads and burying buildings. Landslides are one of the most dangerous natural events because they can happen anywhere in the world. They can occur on every type of surface, from hard rock to soft sand, and can even happen on underwater slopes.

A landslide can travel down a slope at speeds up to 35 miles per hour! That's about as fast as you can ride your bike downhill! Anything that gets in the way of a landslide, from trees to cars, will get carried along as it goes.

 Complete the exercise.

Test your knowledge

Answer T for true or F for false.

(1) Landslides are often caused by natural factors, such as heavy rain or earthquakes.

Ans.

(2) Landslides do not occur suddenly because hard rocks and soil always move slowly down a slope.

Ans.

(3) Landslides can cause rocks and soil to slide across roads and buildings, causing serious damage.

Ans.

Landslides

Think!

Can human activity increase the chances of a landslide happening?

Check

 Read the key points below. When you finish, check the box.

Key Points: Landslide Causes

There are multiple factors that can affect the stability of a slope, but gravity plays a big part in causing loose rocks and soil to slide. **Gravity**, or the force that pulls all objects toward the Earth, is a common factor in natural events like landslides. It is the same force that brought down the block tower.

Gravity isn't the only force that brought down the block tower. Just like when you bumped the tower, and added another force to the situation, landslides also need a second force, or trigger, other than gravity to happen. The actions below can all create an unstable slope that is more vulnerable to landslides.

Natural Hazards:
Other natural hazards such as earthquakes or volcanic eruptions, like you learned about in Chapter 3, can also create higher chances of landslides.

When an **earthquake** hits an area it can shake loose soil and rock from the sides of mountains or hills and cause a strong landslide.

When a volcano erupts, it causes dirt, mud, and ash to slide down its sides, and this can destroy nearby houses, roads and communities.

Rainfall:
Heavy rain is a major cause of landslides. It can cause soil and rocks to loosen and slide down a slope. Rainfall can also cause erosion which can be a contributing factor to a landslide. If rain erodes the mountainside or hillside, a slope can become steeper which can lead to a higher chance of landslides.

Rock Type:
Sometimes the type of rock in an area can increase the chances of a landslide. If the rock is soft like limestone, it could be eroded or loosened more easily than a harder type of rock. This leads to more unstable slopes where landslides can happen.

Construction:
Human activity such as construction or demolition can damage nearby land and lead to landslides. Human activity like deforestation can also leave hillsides vulnerable to landslides because there are fewer plant roots to help hold soil and rocks in place .

 Complete the exercise.

Test your knowledge

Choose three actions that can raise the risk of landslides.

A. heavy rain

B. high temperatures

C. earthquakes

D. demolition and construction

Ans. [,   ,   ]

Chapter 6
Landslides

Think!

What should you do if a landslide occurs in your area?

Check!

📖 Read the key points below. When you finish, check the box.

Key Points: Landslide Prevention and Safety

Since landslides can happen suddenly, it is important to be aware of areas where landslides might occur. Scientists and engineers often monitor such areas. They measure the rainfall in an area and how steep the slopes are to help determine if a landslide is likely to occur.

They also look for physical signs that show an area's risk of having a landslide, such as ground that is cracking or buckling where it hasn't before, places where telephone poles or deck beams are tilting, or areas where the road or land appears to be sinking.

To help prevent landslides, engineers have developed technologies such as nets, anchors, and retaining walls to support slopes that are at risk.

Nets – help prevent rocks and debris from falling onto roads.

Anchors – are drilled into at risk slopes to help hold and stabilize the land.

Retaining Walls – are built to keep unstable slopes from falling onto roadways or structures.

In case prevention efforts don't work, it is also important for people to develop evacuation plans should a landslide happen in their area. When you develop an evacuation plan, you need a safe place to go and also to make sure you have essential supplies you can carry with you. Remember, people need food, water, and shelter to survive. It is also a good idea to have first aid equipment in case someone is hurt.

✏️ Complete the exercise.

Test your knowledge

Which of the following contains an error?

A. Engineers have developed nets, anchors and walls to prevent landslides.

B. Since landslides occur suddenly, it is useless for people to make evacuation plans.

C. When planning an evacuation plan in an emergency, we should make sure that we have the supplies needed to survive, such as water and food. In addition, it is necessary to know in advance of a safe place to go to.

LANDSLIDE HAZARD AREA

Ans.

Chapter 6
Landslides

 Use the word box below to fill in the blanks and review key vocabulary.

Review the Key Points

A [ ] is a large movement of material, such as rock, soil, or mud, down the slope of a hill, a cliff, or a mountainside. Landslides can happen suddenly, due to changes in the stability or strength of their [ ]. Although, sometimes land moves slowly down a mountainside over a longer period of time.

When a landslide happens it can cause serious damage to the surrounding land and communities, by blocking roads and burying buildings. Landslides are one of the most dangerous natural events because they can happen anywhere in the world.

There are multiple factors that can affect the stability of a slope, but [ ] plays a big part in causing loose rocks and soil to slide. Gravity, or the force that pulls all objects toward the Earth, is a common factor in natural events like landslides.

Landslides also need a second force, or trigger, other than gravity to happen. (e.g. natural hazards, rainfall, type of rock, and construction)

Since landslides can happen suddenly, it is important to be aware of areas where landslides might occur. Scientists and engineers often [ ] such areas.

Engineers have developed technologies such as nets, anchors, and retaining walls to support slopes that are at risk.

In case prevention efforts don't work, it is also important for people to develop [ ] plans should a landslide happen in their area.

slopes / monitor / gravity / landslide / evacuation

Complete the exercise.

Math Mission

City Z has received heavy rains in the two days since May 5, and residents are worried about the possibility of landslides. The graphs on the right show precipitation on May 5 and 6 on slopes A, B and C.

(1) What was the precipitation on Slope A on May 5? Ans. [ ] mm

(2) What was the precipitation on Slope B on May 6? Ans. [ ] mm

(3) What was the amount of precipitation in two days on Slope C? Ans. [ ] mm

(4) Which slope had the highest amount of precipitation in two days? Ans. [ ]

Chapter 6
Landslides

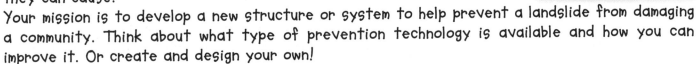

Read the mission. Then, answer the following questions to help you with your solution.

The Mission

Landslides can be harmful to people and communities. Engineers have developed different ways to prevent them and help lessen the damage they can cause.

Your mission is to develop a new structure or system to help prevent a landslide from damaging a community. Think about what type of prevention technology is available and how you can improve it. Or create and design your own!

Before you design...THINK!

1. Describe the mission in your own words.

2. Brainstorm your solution. Write your notes in the space below.

   Use the following questions to guide your thinking:

   (1) Would you use existing technology in your design? Or do you want to create something new to improve protection?

   (2) What type of materials could you use? Would it be better to use rigid materials or flexible materials?

Landslides

Read the mission. Then, draw and evaluate your solution.

The Mission

Your mission is to develop a tool or system to help prevent a landslide from damaging your town. Think about what type of prevention technology is available or create and design your own!

Design   Draw or write your solution below.

Evaluate

Evaluate your landslide protection or prevention system. Do you think it would work? Why or why not? Do you think you need to include safety precautions or evacuation plans along with your device?

Chapter 7
Natural Resources for Energy

Think!

What do you think when you hear the phrase "natural resources"?

Check

 Read the key points. When you finish, check the box.

Key Points: Natural Resources

Ever wonder where the gasoline to power a car comes from? Or how water can be used to power a generator?

A lot of the energy we use every day comes from natural resources. Natural resources are different resources that exist in nature. We use them to power our cars, homes, toys, and most other devices around us.

Some examples of natural resources we use are: coal, oil, wood, water, sunlight, and wind. Here you will learn more about coal and oil, two of the natural resources we use most often to power our world.

Coal: Coal is different from rocks made of only minerals. Coal is made of plant matter, and undergoes many changes before it becomes the black and shiny substance we burn for fuel. While it looks like a normal rock, it is actually made of plants which grew hundreds of millions of years ago, and were put under extreme pressure at the bottom of lakes and swamps. The pressure they were under was so intense it changed the physical material in the plants and minerals into coal. Nowadays, we dig the coal up from where it was created and use it as a fuel source.

Oil: Oil is made of the remains of ancient living things that slowly piled up on the bottom of the ocean and were covered by sediment and sand. This made it possible for bacteria in the soil along with extreme heat and pressure to change the material into oil. Oil is found underground . It is extracted with giant drilling machines that are strong enough penetrate into the Earth. When oil comes out of the ground, it usually looks black or dark brown.

 Complete the exercise.

Test your knowledge

(1) Which would be considered a natural resource commonly used for energy?

A. wood   B. glass   C. fabric   D. plastic

Ans.

(2) Which of the following is a natural resources that comes from plants that died millions of years ago?

A. wood   B. plastic   C. coal   D. wind

Ans.

Chapter 7
Natural Resources for Energy

Think!

What are the advantages and disadvantages of natural non-renewable resources such as coal and oil?

 Read the key points below. When you finish, check the box.

Key Points: Issues with Non-renewable Resources

The way we get these natural resources and turn them into energy is different for each resource. Coal and oil can supply us with a lot of energy, but getting them can also cause problems.

Digging for coal can be unsafe for miners. Miners breathe in coal dust as they work which can cause illnesses later in life. They can also get trapped in a mine if it collapses. Additionally, in order to use coal as a source of energy, it has to be burned. This adds to air pollution, which can have negative impacts on the Earth's atmosphere as you read in Chapter 5.

There are problems involved in drilling for oil too. Drilling can sometimes cause oil spills, which are harmful to the environment, especially to the plants and animals that live nearby. And like coal, oil needs to be burned to release energy and that causes harmful air pollution.

Another major problem with some natural resources such as coal and oil is that they are non-renewable. A **non-renewable resource** is a natural resource that is gone forever once it is used up. When coal or oil are burned they are converted into other substances which release energy and cannot be turned back into their original form and used again.

✏ Complete the exercise.

Test your knowledge

Answer T for true or F for false.

(1) Coal and oil have the advantage of providing us with a lot of energy.

Ans.

(2) Coal and oil have the disadvantage of causing air pollution because they have to be burned to produce energy.

Ans.

(3) Coal and oil have the advantage of being reusable natural resources.

Ans.

Chapter 7
Natural Resources for Energy

Think!

Do you know which natural resources are renewable?

 Read the key points below. When you finish, check the box.

 Check

Key Points: Renewable Resources

Since there are problems with non-renewable natural resources like coal and oil, scientists and engineers have developed ways to use renewable resources for energy instead. **Renewable resources** are resources that can be used repeatedly and are replaced naturally.

Some examples of renewable resources are wind, solar or sun, and water.

Water or Hydropower:
Hydropower is power produced by using the energy created by running water. For example, water flowing in a river can be used to spin a wheel in a machine called a generator. The generator converts the energy of the moving water to electricity. People will often build dams to block and control the flow of water in a river and use it to power generators. But, hydropower can be created anywhere there is running water.

Wind Power:
Wind power is created by harnessing wind. When wind turns the blades of a windmill, a generator converts the energy of the spinning blades into power we can use. Wind is a renewable natural resource because we can never run out of wind!

Solar Power:
Solar power is created using sunlight. Solar panels are used to capture energy from the sun's rays and turn it into power for your home.

 Complete the exercise.

Test your knowledge

Match effective ways to convert each renewable resource to usable energy.

(1) water or hydropower ●　　　　　　　● solar panel

(2) wind power ●　　　　　　　● dam

(3) solar power ●　　　　　　　● windmill

Chapter 7
Natural Resources for Energy

Use the word box below to fill in the blanks and review key vocabulary.

Review the Key Points

A lot of the energy we use every day comes from [   ] resources. Natural resources are different resources that exist in nature. We use them to power our cars, homes, toys, and most other devices around us.

Some examples of natural resources we use are: coal, oil, wood, water, sunlight, and wind.

The way we get these natural resources and turn them into [   ] is different for each resource. Coal and [   ] can supply us with a lot of energy, but getting them can also cause problems.

When coal or oil are burned they are converted into other substances which release energy and cannot be turned back into their [   ] form and used again.

Since there are problems with non-renewable natural resources like coal and oil, scientists and engineers have developed ways to use [   ] resources for energy instead. Renewable resources are resources that can be used repeatedly and are replaced naturally.

original / natural / renewable / energy / oil

Complete the exercise.

Math Mission

Answer the following questions about Renewable energy.

(1) There are residential solar panels with a power generation capacity of 100 kW per panel. How many kilowatts of power will be generated when you install eight of these? "kW (kilowatt)" is a unit of electric power.

Ans. [   ] kW

(2) One windmill can produce enough electricity to power 1,500 homes for a year. How many windmills does it take to produce enough electricity to power 4,500 homes for a year?

Ans. [   ] windmills

Chapter 7
Natural Resources for Energy

 Read the mission. Then, answer the following questions to help you with your solution.

The Mission

Think about where you live. What natural resources near you could be used for energy? Do you think your area could benefit from using renewable natural resources?
Design a plan to bring renewable energy to or to increase the use of renewable energy in your area.

Before you design...THINK!

1. Describe the mission in your own words.

2. Brainstorm about a solution. Write your notes in the space below.

   Use the following questions to guide your thinking:

   (1) What natural resources are plentiful in your area?
   (2) Does your town already use renewable energy resources? How can you improve on the use of renewable resources?
   (3) If your area does not use renewable energy sources, how can you get people to use them?

Natural Resources for Energy

💡 Read the mission. Then, draw and evaluate your solution.

The Mission

Design a plan to bring renewable energy to or to increase the use of renewable energy in your area.

Design

Draw or write about your solution below.

Evaluate

Evaluate your plan. How can you get more people to participate in your plan? Do you think people will want to help you with your plan? What do you want the outcome of your plan to be?

Chapter 8
Disposing of Waste

Think!

What do you do with things you no longer need?

Check

 Read the key points. When you finish, check the box.

Key Points: What is waste?

Do you ever think about what happens to the scrap paper you used for your math homework and then threw away? It will probably be thrown out with the rest of your garbage. Objects like used paper, discarded food and other things you throw away are called **waste**.

We can find a variety of waste in our everyday lives. When you eat a banana you typically throw the peel away when you're done. You do the same thing with the wrapper from a candy bar. Both get thrown in the trash when you have finished your snack, but there is one big difference between these two pieces of waste.

The banana peel will decay, or break down, over a few months and its nutrients can be used by the soil. The candy bar wrapper will not break down as quickly. It is made of plastic which can take 20 years or more to break down and will not add any nutrients to the soil.

Most of the waste or trash humans throw out is not **biodegradable** like the banana peel, and will not naturally break down into the soil. Paper, plastic, and glass all take a long time to break down when they

are thrown away. They are non-biodegradable, because even when they break down they are not adding nutrients to the earth. When biodegradable and non-biodegradable materials are thrown out together it can slow down the natural break-down of the biodegradable material.

In the US alone, people make around 1 million pounds of waste materials each year! Can you imagine how much waste that is?

 Complete the exercise.

Test your knowledge

Choose all of the following waste materials that are not biodegradable (do not decay or break down naturally) and will accumulate without being able to nourish the soil.

A. plastic

B. banana peel

C. glass

D. paper

Ans. [ ]

Disposing of Waste

Think!

Do you think about the waste you throw away? Is it mainly biodegradable or not?

 Read the key points below. When you finish, check the box.

Check

Key Points: Waste Disposal

People have developed various methods to dispose of the large amount of garbage and waste they create. Recycling, burning, and burying are a few examples.

Recycling

Recycling is the best option for disposing of plastic, can, glass, and paper waste materials. While paper products take a few months to break down naturally, plastic and aluminum can take hundreds of years, and glass products may never fully decompose! This is why recycling is key. It can reduce the amount of paper, glass, can, and plastic materials that end up in landfills because these products can be recycled into something we can use again.

Burning

Burning is another way that people get rid of natural waste like paper, tree branches, and grass clippings. Burning waste can help reduce the amount of waste that ends up in landfills because it reduces solid waste to ash that takes up less space. However, burning non-natural waste can release dangerous gases and chemicals into the air. These gases can pollute the air people breathe, so engineers have developed ways to contain the harmful gases and clean the air before it is released.

Burying

Burying is another method of getting rid of waste. This method is normally used for dangerous and hazardous waste such as radioactive waste. This is the kind of waste that people should not touch or be near, so burying it in sealed containers is one of the safest ways to keep people from coming into contact with it.

 Complete the exercise.

Test your knowledge

Choose the best way to dispose of the following.

A. recycling   B. burning   C. burying

(1) To dispose of radioactive waste from a chemical plant.

Ans. ☐

(2) To dispose of 100 cans of soda after a birthday party.

Ans. ☐

(3) To dispose of tree branches cut from an old tree.

Ans. ☐

Chapter 8
Disposing of Waste

Think!

Are landfills a good way to dispose of waste? Can you think of a better way?

📖 Read the key points below. When you finish, check the box.

Check

Key Points: Landfills

Besides recycling, burning, and burying, the most common way people dispose of waste is in **landfills**. Landfills are large pits typically lined with clay, soil and plastic that are filled layer by layer with waste. They were created as a safe way to dispose of waste and garbage so as it breaks down it does not harm the environment and people around it.

Today, some engineers have developed landfills lined with a heavy-duty plastic to prevent dangerous chemicals or decaying materials from leaking into the ground. Besides the plastic lining, every layer of garbage is compressed and covered with a thin topping of soil to prevent air and pests from getting at the garbage.

Although landfills have been designed to be a safe option for waste disposal they can still have issues. Landfills that are not vented properly can cause a dangerous build up of methane, a type of gas that can be harmful to people and the atmosphere. Other issues can occur if liquid waste leaks through the seams in the plastic liner and gets into our ground water. This can contaminate the ground water and make people sick. It can also harm plants and animals in the surrounding area. A last major problem with landfills is that they cannot hold an endless amount of waste. Landfills often become full and need to be closed up. This leads to the creation of more landfills to continue collecting the large amount of garbage people produce.

Gases such as methane generated in landfills are collected by special equipment and pumped through pipes into a storage facility to be used as an energy source.

✏️ Complete the exercise.

Test your knowledge

Answer the questions below about the reading.

(1) What is a landfill?

A. a large pit filled layer by layer with garbage

B. a place where waste is collected to be reused

C. a place where waste is sorted

D. a large factory that produces waste

Ans. ▢

(2) Which is not a possible problem with a landfill?

A. harmful liquid waste leaking into the ground

B. build-up of methane gas

C. helping waste break down faster

D. endangering nearby plants and animals

Ans. ▢

Chapter 8
Disposing of Waste

✏ **Use the word box below to fill in the blanks and review key vocabulary.**

Review the Key Points

Objects like used paper, discarded food and other things you don't want are called [   ].

Most of the waste or trash humans throw out is not [   ] and will not naturally break down into the soil. Paper, plastic, and glass all take a long time to break down when they are thrown away. They are non-biodegradable, because even when they break down they are not adding nutrients to the earth. When biodegradable and non-biodegradable materials are thrown out together it can slow down the natural break-down of the biodegradable material.

People have developed various methods to dispose of the large amount of garbage and waste they create. Recycling, burning, and burying are a few examples.

Recycling is the best option for disposing of plastic, glass, and paper waste materials. Burning is another way that people get rid of natural waste like paper, tree branches, and grass clippings. [   ] is another method of getting rid of waste. This method is normally used for dangerous and hazardous waste such as radioactive waste.

[   ] are large pits typically lined with clay, soil and plastic that are filled layer by layer with waste. They were created as a safe way to dispose of waste and garbage so as it breaks down it does not harm the environment and people around it.

Although, landfills have been designed to be a safe option for waste disposal they can still have issues.

> waste / burying / landfills / biodegradable

⊞ **Complete the exercise.**

Math Mission

Use the chart to answer the questions below about the length of time it takes different materials to decompose or break down in a landfill.

(1) How long does it take an orange peel to decompose?

Ans. [   ]

(2) How long would it take a newspaper to decompose?

Ans. [   ]

(3) What would decompose first? An aluminum soda can or a plastic soda bottle?

Ans. [   ]

Estimated Decomposition Rates

Paper	2-4 weeks
Leaves	1-3 months
Orange Peel	3-6 months
Milk Carton	5 years
Plastic Bag	10-20 years
Aluminum Can	200-400 years
Plastic 6 Pk Ring	400-500 years
Plastic Bottle	400-500 years
Glass Bottle	500 years- forever?
Styrofoam	never?

Disposing of Waste

 Read the mission. Then, answer the following questions to help you with your solution.

The Mission

Waste is a major problem in the US and around the world. While landfills are a good option for disposing of waste, they are not perfect. Landfills can leak, become full, and harm the environment.
Your mission is to design a better method to help solve the waste problem.

Before you design...THINK!

1. Describe the mission in your own words.

2. Brainstorm about a solution. Write your notes in the space below.

   Use the following questions to guide your thinking:

   (1) What are the problems with modern landfills? How can you fix these problems with your design?
   (2) Can you think of a new way to dispose of waste? What materials could you use?

Chapter 8
Disposing of Waste

💡 Read the mission. Then, draw and evaluate your solution.

The Mission

Waste is a major problem in the US and around the world. While landfills are a good option for disposing of waste, they are not perfect. Landfills can leak, become full, and harm the environment.
Your mission is to design a better method to help solve the waste problem.

Design   Draw or write your solution below.

Evaluate

Evaluate your new landfill or waste disposal system. Do you think it would work? Did you use existing technology or did you create your own waste disposal system?

Chapter 1 Severe Weather

1

Test your knowledge

(1) B   (2) C

2

Test your knowledge

(1) C   (2) B   (3) A   (4) D

3

Test your knowledge

(1) T   (2) F   (3) T

4

Review the Key Points

atmosphere / severe weather / shutters / alert

Math Mission

(1) 30 °F

(2) $110 - 70 = 40$ Ans. 40 °F

(3) $110 - 30 = 80$ Ans. 80 °F

5 (Sample Response)

Before you design... THINK!

1. Create a protection system or device to keep my house safe from bad weather.

2. I think I will improve on the hurricane shutters and figure out how to use tools to warn people about the hurricane.

   Maybe I will use a warning system like a siren in my town or something that is sent to your phone.

6 (Sample Response)

Design

My device would attach to hurricane shutters on people's homes. When the wind blew at a certain speed, the device would make the shutters close over the window. This would help keep people safe.

Evaluate

I think my system will work. I think a problem could be that the wind sensors would close the window with any high winds, not just during a hurricane.

Chapter 2 Beach Erosion

7

Test your knowledge

(1) weathering

(2) erosion

(3) people

8

Test your knowledge

(1) F   (2) T   (3) F

9

Test your knowledge

(1) C   (2) B   (3) A

10

Review the Key Points

Weathering / Erosion / beach sand / Strong winds

Math Mission

(1) $2 \times 10 = 20$ Ans. 20 feet

(2) $36 \div 6 = 6$ Ans. 6 years

(3) $24 \div 4 = 6$ Ans. 6 trucks

11 (Sample Response)

Before you design... THINK!

1. Create a plan to help save the beach from further erosion and to restore it.

2. - bring more sand to the beach as a start

   - create a barrier to keep the sand on the beach and not let it be washed away

   - mesh netting? - use a semi-solid barrier that lets water through, but not sand

12 (Sample Response)

Design

I would build a mesh barrier that was designed to keep sand on the beach but let water through. It would be attached to ropes on the shore and people could pull it in to bring back the sand that washed away.

Evaluate

My design could be improved by finding a natural way to help stop beach erosion instead of adding manmade objects to the beach.

Chapter 3 Tectonic Plates

13

Test your knowledge

(1) A   (2) C

14

Test your knowledge

(1) C   (2) B   (3) D

15

Test your knowledge

(1) B   (2) A

16

Review the Key Points

mantle / Tectonic plates / earthquake / epicenter / seismograph

Math Mission

(1) 1000   (2) A   (3) C

17 (Sample Response)

Before you design... THINK!

1. Design a device or plan to help earthquake proof buildings.
2. I could improve existing technology to help make homes safer.

   One existing technology I could improve on is what material buildings are made of. Plastic is a flexible and sturdy material I could use in my design.

18 (Sample Response)

Design

I would design a way to build part of my structure out of strong and flexible plastic that would bend and move as the earthquake shook the building. It would have flexible plastic joints that connected strong metal beams. The metal beams would hold up the structure and the plastic joints would help it bend.

Evaluate

I think my design would work because it would make the structure more resistant to the earthquake's shock waves. I think one issue would be that it would be hard to test and make sure my idea works to keep a building safe during a real earthquake.

Chapter 4 Flooding

19

Test your knowledge

B

20

Test your knowledge

(1)
(2)
(3)

21

Test your knowledge

(1)
(2)
(3)

22

Review the Key Points

flood / heavy rain / floodplain / dikes

Math Mission

(1) A

(2) $100 \times 3 = 300$ Ans. 300 m

(3) $500 \div 100 = 5$ Ans. 5 cm

23 (Sample Response)

Before you design... THINK!

1. Create a plan to keep people safe from floods or stop flooding from damaging the community.
2. - build something to help prevent a flood
   - stop rising water from overflowing the river bank
   - design something to divert flood waters

24 (Sample Response)

Design

For this mission, I would improve on existing flood barriers. I would build a levee to prevent water from reaching the town, but it would have some slides or chutes coming down from the top that collected the overflowing water and directed it to a smaller reservoir away from the town. The flood water could then be used by the people in the town for energy or farming.

Evaluate

I think my design could work as long as the overflow water went into the chutes and did not overflow past them. It would not work as well during a flash flood.

Chapter 5 **Changing Climates**

25

Test your knowledge
(1) F   (2) T   (3) F

26

Test your knowledge
(1) D   (2) C   (3) A   (4) B

27

Test your knowledge
(1) T   (2) F   (3) T

28

Review the Key Points
Climate / sea level / Global warming / greenhouse effect

Math Mission
(1) $3 \times 5 = 15$ Ans. 15 minutes
(2) $60 \div 3 = 20$ Ans. 20 saplings
(3) $30 \div 3 = 10$

    10 (number of saplings for one adult can plant in 30 minutes) $\times$ 3 (number of adults) = 30
                           Ans. 30 saplings

29 (Sample Response)

Before you design... THINK!
1. Create a plan to inform people about changing climates.
2. I would need to do more research on how changing climates affect the world around me and my community. I could create a monthly newsletter and send it to all of my community in the mail or by email.

30 (Sample Response)

Design
My plan to inform my community about changing climates would be to create a monthly newsletter that I could send by email or mail to help inform people about it. The newsletter would explain what is happening and tell people ways to help.

Evaluate
I think my newsletter would be successful in informing people in my community about the dangers of the changing climate. I think it may be hard to get people to read it or sign up to get it, but once they do I think it will help.

Chapter 6 **Landslides**

31

Test your knowledge
(1) T   (2) F   (3) T

32

Test your knowledge
A, C, D

33

Test your knowledge
B

34

Review the Key Points
landslide / slopes / gravity / monitor / evacuation

Math Mission
(1) 200 mm   (2) 150 mm   (3) 400 mm   (4) A

35 (Sample Response)

Before you design... THINK!
1. Create a piece of technology or plan to help prevent landslides from damaging a community.
2. I will use current technology to create my protection system and keep people and the town safe from landslides.
   I will use materials that are flexible, so if they are hit by a landslide they bounce back.
   I will also create an escape plan to help people get to safety.

36 (Sample Response)

Design
My plan would be to create flexible sensors that could be put in holes in the hillside to help measure the land sliding. They would be flexible plastic or rubber so they could move with the ground and alert scientists if the ground slides too much. The scientists can read the measurements and help determine if a landslide could happen there.

Evaluate
I think one issue would be if the sensors aren't dug deep enough into the hillside they could be in the landslide.

Chapter 7 Natural Resources for Energy

37

Test your knowledge
(1) A   (2) C

38

Test your knowledge
(1) T   (2) T   (3) F

39

Test your knowledge

(1)
(2)
(3)

40

Review the Key Points
natural / energy / oil / original / renewable

Math Mission
(1) $100 \times 8 = 800$ Ans. 800 kW
(2) $4500 \div 1500 = 3$ Ans. 3 windmills

41 (Sample Response)

Before you design... THINK!
1. Create a renewable energy plan for your town.
2. Figure out what type of renewable energy to use in the plan.
   Where I live is really sunny, so I will use solar energy.
   How can I distribute my plan in my community?

42 (Sample Response)

Design
Create a solar panel field that the whole town can access power from, to help people use renewable energy.

Evaluate
Some people in the community might not want to be part of the plan. They may be more concerned with what it will cost to build than with how it will help.

PLEASE DO NOT WRITE IN THIS BOOK.

Chapter 8 Disposing of Waste

43

Test your knowledge
A, C, D

44

Test your knowledge
(1) C   (2) A   (3) B

45

Test your knowledge
(1) A   (2) C

46

Review the Key Points
waste / biodegradable / Burying / Landfills

Math Mission
(1) 3-6 months
(2) 2-4 weeks
(3) aluminum soda can

47 (Sample Response)

Before you design... THINK!
1. Create a better way to get rid of waste.
2. Some problems with modern landfills are leaks and dangerous chemicals.
   My design will address these issues with better materials.
   Create a plan that offers people an incentive for recycling or composting.
   Can we encourage people to make less waste?

48 (Sample Response)

Design
Create a conveyer belt that will sort the garbage so less waste ends up in landfills. This will help landfill have less waste. Add a second layer of material that will absorb any of the liquid waste that tries to leak through the plastic lining. It will help stop leaks from getting into the dirt and ground water.

Evaluate
I think my technology will help less trash go to the landfill, because recyclable and compost material will not end up in the landfill and can get reused. Then, my absorbing layer will help keep the land around the landfill safe from the material that is thrown away.